21
SUPER
SIMPLE
Geology
EXPERIMENTS

Rebecca W. Keller, PhD

REAL SCIENCE 4 Kids

Illustrations: Janet Moneymaker
Photographs: Rebecca W. Keller, PhD

21 Super Simple Geology Experiments
ISBN: 978-1-941181-26-3

Published by Gravitas Publications, Inc.
www.gravitaspublications.com

What Are Super Simple Science Experiments?

Super Simple Science Experiments are experiments that each focus on one aspect of scientific investigation. Doing science requires the development of different types of skills. These skills include the ability to make good observations, turning observations into questions and/or hypotheses, building and using models, analyzing data, using controls, and using different science tools including computers.

Super Simple Science Experiments break down the steps of scientific investigation so that you can focus on one aspect of scientific inquiry. The experiments are simple and easy to do, yet they are *real* science experiments that help you develop the skills needed for *real* scientific investigations.

Each experiment is one page long and lists an objective, the materials needed, a brief outline of the experiment, and any graphics or illustrations needed for the experiment. The skill being explored is shown in the upper right hand corner of each page.

The recommended companion book, *Super Simple Science Experiments Laboratory Notebook*, is a great place to record all the results of your experiments. It contains blank pages, lined pages, graph pages, and boxes for drawings.

Getting Started

Below is a list of the materials for all the geology experiments in this book. You can collect all the materials ahead of time and place them in a storage bin or drawer.

Materials at a Glance	
Super Simple Science Experiments Laboratory Notebook backpack balloon chalk, 2 pieces compass container, plastic freezer dough, stiff, or modeling clay hand lens hose with spray nozzle or bucket of water jar, 2 jar with lid knife milk carton, 2 liter (1/2 gallon), 2 nail, steel pencil pencils, colored penny, copper plant, small vegetable or herb, 2-3 of the same type plaster of Paris	rocks, igneous* (basalt, pumice, obsidian, granite) rocks, metamorphic* (quartzite, marble, gneiss, slate) rocks, minerals* (choose several—calcite, quartz, hematite, mica, graphite, talc, pyrite, gypsum) rocks, sedimentary* (sandstone, limestone, breccia, shale) rocks, student-collected ruler snack food soil samples, student-collected soil additives (e.g., clay, silt, sand, organic matter) stones, three approx. 2.5 cm (1 inch) streak plate* treasure (toy, coin, etc.) trowel, garden, or spoon vinegar, apple cider, 60 ml (1/4 cup) water water bottle water softener, 1 tbsp. (e.g., Calgon liquid)

* A streak plate and a rock kit that contains samples of minerals, igneous, sedimentary, and metamorphic rocks can be purchased from Home Science Tools   http://www.hometrainingtools.com/   or a local rock shop

Table of Contents

1. Observing Your World

Objective

To observe your surroundings and notice the geological features near you.

Materials

pencil
Super Simple Science Experiments Laboratory Notebook

Experiment

❶ Take your notebook and pencil and carry them with you while you go outside and walk around your house. Notice what is nearby. Is there dirt? Grass? Concrete? In your Laboratory Notebook, record what you see.

❷ Next, walk around your neighborhood. Notice if there are trees, hills, paved or dirt roads, rocks, boulders, ditches, or any other features you find interesting. Record what you see

❸ Now that you have observed the area around your house and neighborhood, draw a map of the area you've explored. Is your house in the center? On one end or the other? Make your map as detailed as possible including buildings, roads, boulders, hills, rivers, or any other features you find interesting.

Results and Conclusions

The first step in learning about geology is to observe the area where you live. By walking around your neighborhood, noticing manmade and geological features that are nearby, taking notes, and making a map of the area you explore, you can begin to learn about the geology of your area.

2. Hidden Treasure

Objective

To explore map making.

Materials

pencil
hidden treasure of your choice (a toy, coin,
    or other favorite object)
Super Simple Science Experiments
    Laboratory Notebook

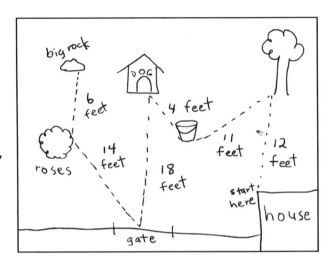

Experiment

❶ Look at the map you created in the first experiment. Choose a section of your map
that is small enough that you can easily measure it. This may be your back or front
yard, the park across the street, or a corner lot on the end of the block. Make a
new map of this area to use as a treasure map. Draw the outline of the area and
add some features.

❷ Use your feet to measure heel-to-toe how long this area is on each side and the
distance between different features. Each of your feet equals "one foot." Mark these
distances on your map.

❸ Pick out something to use as a treasure to hide. Measure the number of feet (your
feet) to a secret spot and mark this on your map. Hide your treasure here.

❹ Give your treasure map to a friend, sibling, parent, or teacher and ask them to use
the map to find the hidden treasure.

Results and Conclusions

Being able to make an accurate map is important for learning about geology. You may
have discovered that making a good map is difficult. It requires looking at lots of
different features and finding a way to accurately measure distance. In this experiment
you tried to create a map that was good enough to have someone else find a hidden
treasure. However, if a map doesn't have enough details, the treaure could be lost!

3. How Hard Are Minerals?

Objective

To identify the hardness of minerals using Mohs scale of mineral hardness.

Mohs Scale of Mineral Hardness

Object	Hardness
fingernail	2.5
copper penny	3
steel nail	5.5
streak plate	6.5

Materials

pencil

several of the following minerals:*
    calcite, quartz, hematite, mica,
    graphite, talc, pyrite, gypsum

copper penny

steel nail

Super Simple Science Experiments Laboratory Notebook

Experiment

❶ In your Laboratory Notebook, create a table with 3 columns and 5 rows. Enter the following column titles in the top row: Mineral Name, Hardness, Notes. Label the remaining rows with the names of the minerals you will test.

❷ Using the Mohs scale of mineral hardness, determine the hardness of each mineral sample and record the value in your table.

❸ Make notes about the features of each mineral sample (color, texture, etc.)

Results and Conclusions

In this experiment you tested the relative hardness of different minerals using the Mohs scale of mineral hardness. The Mohs scale of mineral hardness is a quick field test used by geologists to help identify different minerals. For example, you will notice that calcite is softer than hematite and mica is softer than pyrite. By being familiar with the relative hardness of some minerals, you can more easily identify minerals you find on a hike or expedition.

* Mineral samples can be purchased from Home Science Tools http://www.hometrainingtools.com/
  or a local rock shop

4. What Color Are Minerals?

Objective

To use a streak plate to examine the color of minerals.

Materials

pencil
several of the following minerals:*
    calcite, quartz, hematite, mica,
    graphite, talc, pyrite, gypsum
streak plate (unglazed white ceramic tile)
Super Simple Science Experiments
    Laboratory Notebook

Photo credit: NASA/JPL

Experiment

❶ In your Laboratory Notebook, create a table with 3 columns and 5 rows. Enter the following column titles in the top row: Mineral Name, Streak Color, Notes. Label the remaining rows with the names of the minerals you will test.

❷ Scratch each mineral firmly across the streak plate. Record the color in the table you made and make notes about the features of the sample.

Results and Conclusions

Another way to help identify minerals is to use a streak test. When a mineral is rubbed firmly across the rough surface of a streak plate, it leaves a streak of colored powder behind. Different minerals will leave different colors on a streak plate. However, many minerals have a white streak, and their streak is not visible on a white streak plate. Also, if the mineral is harder than the streak plate, it will not leave a streak but may scratch the plate. By becoming familiar with the color a particular mineral leaves on a streak plate, you can better identify minerals you find on a hike or expedition.

* Mineral samples and a streak plate can be purchased from Home Science Tools
  (http://www.hometrainingtools.com/) or a local rock shop

5. Testing Rocks

Objective

To identify the minerals found in rocks by using the Mohs scale of mineral hardness and the streak test.

Materials

pencil

several of the following minerals:*
   calcite, quartz, hematite, mica,
   graphite, talc, pyrite, gypsum

streak plate

copper penny

steel nail

Super Simple Science Experiments
   Laboratory Notebook

Mohs Scale of Mineral Hardness

Object	Hardness
fingernail	2.5
copper penny	3
steel nail	5.5
streak plate	6.5

Experiment

❶ In your Laboratory Notebook, create a table with 4 columns and 5 rows. Enter the following column titles in the top row: Mineral Name, Streak Color, Hardness, Notes. Label the remaining rows with the names of the minerals you will test.

❷ Scratch each mineral firmly across the streak plate. Record the color in your table.

❸ Using the Mohs scale of mineral hardness, determine the hardness of each sample and record the value in the table. Make notes about the features of each sample.

Results and Conclusions

Because these two tests are quick and easy to execute and the materials needed to perform them are easy to carry, field geologists and hobbyists use both the streak test and the Moh's scale of hardness to help quickly identify minerals they find in the field.

* Mineral samples and a streak plate can be purchased from Home Science Tools (http://www.hometrainingtools. com/) or a local rock shop

6. Igneous Rocks

observation

Objective

To identify igneous rocks and examine their texture and color.

Materials

pencil

hand lens

the following igneous rocks:

    basalt, pumice, obsidian, granite*

Super Simple Science Experiments

    Laboratory Notebook

Igneous Rock

Textures	Colors
❶ minerals are visible to the naked eye and form a mosaic	❶ mostly dark colored rock
❷ minerals are too small to see without a hand lens	❷ mostly light colored rock
❸ texture is sponge-like with cavities and holes	❸ blend of dark and light colored rock
❹ texture is glassy	

Experiment

❶ In your Laboratory Notebook, create a table with 4 columns and 3 rows.

❷ Enter the following column titles in the top row: Basalt, Pumice, Obsidian, Granite.

❸ In the 2nd row record the texture of each rock.

❹ In the 3rd row record the color of each rock.

Results and Conclusions

Igneous rocks are formed when hot magma solidifies either below the surface of the Earth's crust or above the surface of the Earth's crust. Igneous rocks that form below the Earth's crust are called intrusive igneous rocks, and igneous rocks that form above the Earth's crust are called extrusive igneous rocks. Intrusive rocks typically have larger grain sizes because they cool more slowly than extrusive rocks.

* A rock kit that contains samples of minerals and igneous, sedimentary, and metamorphic rocks can be purchased from Home Science Tools http://www.hometrainingtools.com/

7. Sedimentary Rocks

Objective

To identify sedimentary rocks and examine their texture and color.

Materials

pencil

hand lens

the following sedimentary rocks:*

sandstone, limestone, breccia, shale

Super Simple Science Experiments

Laboratory Notebook

Sedimentary Rock

Textures	Colors
❶ has cemented gravel, sand, or mud	❶ mostly dark colored rock
❷ no visible grains, smooth texture	❷ mostly light colored rock
❸ contains shell fragments, plant material, or fossil parts	❸ blend of dark and light colored rock

Experiment

❶ In your Laboratory Notebook, create a table with 4 columns and 3 rows. Enter the following column titles in the top row: Sandstone, Limestone, Breccia, Shale.

❷ In the 2nd row record the texture of each rock.

❸ In the 3rd row record the color of each rock.

Results and Conclusions

Sedimentary rocks are formed from preexisiting rocks such as igneous rocks, other sedimentary rocks, and metamorphic rocks that have been weathered or worn away by both physical and chemical interactions. There are two main types of sedimentary rocks—detrital and chemical. Detrital rocks are rocks that have been formed from layers of weathered debris, and chemical sedimentary rocks are those rocks that have been formed when minerals precipitate from the solution they were dissolved in.

*A rock kit that contains samples of minerals and igneous, sedimentary, and metamorphic rocks can be purchased from Home Science Tools http://www.hometrainingtools.com/

8. Metamorphic Rocks

observation

Objective

To identify metamorphic rocks and examine their texture and color.

Metamorphic Rock	
Textures	**Colors**
❶ layered with small grains	❶ mostly dark colored rock
❷ layered with large grains	❷ mostly light colored rock
❸ not layered with no visible grains	❸ blend of dark and light colored rock

Materials

pencil
hand lens
the following metamorphic rocks:*
    quartzite, marble, gneiss, slate
Super Simple Science Experiments
    Laboratory Notebook

Experiment

❶ In your Laboratory Notebook, create a table with 4 columns and 3 rows. Enter the following column titles in the top row: Quartzite, Marble, Gneiss, Slate.

❷ In the 2nd row record the texture of each rock.

❸ In the 3rd row record the color of each rock.

Results and Conclusions

Metamorphic rocks are rocks that have been modified by heat, pressure, and chemical processes, usually deep inside the Earth's crust. There are two basic types of metamorphic rock: foliated (layered) and non-foliated (not layered). Metamorphic rocks such as gneiss and slate are foliated and have visible and distinct layers. Slate can be split into large slabs. Marble and quartzite are non-foliated metamorphic rocks and do not have any visible layers.

* A rock kit that contains samples of minerals and igneous, sedimentary, and metamorphic rocks can be purchased from Home Science Tools http://www.hometrainingtools.com/

9. Identifying Rocks

Objective

To identify unknown rocks by examining their texture and color.

Materials

pencil, colored pencils
hand lens
a set of rocks collected from your backyard, nearby park, or hiking trail
Super Simple Science Experiments Laboratory Notebook

Rock Types		
Igneous	**Sedimentary**	**Metamorphic**
Texture ❶ intrusive: large grain size ❷ extrusive: small grain size ❸ sponge-like: cavities, holes ❹ glassy **Color** ❶ dark colored ❷ light colored ❸ mixture of light and dark	**Texture** ❶ detrital: cemented gravel, sand, mud ❷ detrital: shell fragments, plant material, fossil parts ❸ chemical: no grains **Color** ❶ dark colored ❷ light colored ❸ mixture of light and dark	**Texture** ❶ foliated: large grain size ❷ foliated: small grain size ❸ non-foliated: no grains **Color** ❶ dark colored ❷ light colored ❸ mixture of light and dark

Experiment

❶ Choose one rock and draw it in your Laboratory Notebook, noting the color, texture, size, and any other characteristic features.

❷ Examine the rock and determine if it is an igneous, sedimentary, or metamorphic rock. Once you have determined the general type of rock, identify the specific type of rock (intrusive or extrusive igneous rock, detrital or chemical sedimentary rock, foliated or non-foliated metamorphic rock).

❸ Repeat Steps ❶-❷ with your other rock samples.

Results and Conclusions

Write your conclusions about how easy or difficult is was to identify your rocks.

10. Soils

Objective

To identify the type of soil that exists in your yard or in a nearby park.

Materials

pencil

jar and garden trowel or spoon

soil sample you have collected from your yard or a nearby park

Super Simple Science Experiments Laboratory Notebook

Experiment

❶ Examine the soil you have collected.

❷ Note the color and texture of the soil.

❸ Create a table in your Laboratory Notebook with 2 columns and 2 rows. In the first row write "Color" in the first column and "Texture" in the second column. Record the color and texture of the soil you've collected.

Types of Soil

Soil Type	Color	Texture
Clay	red, brown, green, gray, yellow, near-black	very fine grains
Sand	gray, brown, white, yellow, black	small grains
Silt	brown, black	fine grains
Loam	gray, white, brown	is a mixture of sand, clay and silt; medium grains
Chalk	gray, white, yellow	white, with stones
Peat	black, brown	flaky with dead organic matter

Results and Conclusions

There are six basic types of soils: clay, silty, sandy, loamy, chalky, and peat. Each soil type has varying size grains and color. Which type is your soil sample?

11. Soil and Water

Objective

To investigate the flow of water through soil.

Materials

pencil
2 liter (1/2 gallon) milk carton
.25-1 liter (1-4 cups) of soil from your
    yard or a nearby park
three approx. 2.5 cm (1 inch) stones
.5 liter (2 cups) of water
Super Simple Science Experiments
    Laboratory Notebook

Experiment

❶ Cut off the top half of the milk carton. Punch three 1.25 cm (1/2 inch) holes in the bottom of the container.

❷ Place the stones on top of the holes. There should be enough space around the holes for water to flow.

❸ Pour the soil into the milk carton and fill it 2/3 of the way to the top.

❹ Pour the water into the soil. Observe how well the water flows out the bottom. Notice if the water gets trapped inside or if the water flows too quickly through the soil. Record your observations in the Laboratory Notebook.

Results and Conclusions

Testing the type of soil for how well it both holds water and drains water is important for preparing soils for growing plants. Sandy and chalky soil will drain the water very quickly. If you have clay or silty soil, the water won't drain very well and may become sticky when wet and hard when it dries out. Knowing what type of soil you have will help you select the right kinds of plants to grow in that soil.

12. Soil and Plants

Objective

To investigate how well plants will grow in your soil.

Materials

pencil
soil container from Experiment 11
small vegetable or herb plant
Super Simple Science Experiments
    Laboratory Notebook

Experiment

❶ Plant a small vegetable or herb plant in your milk carton container.

❷ Place the container where it will get a good amount of sunlight and allow the plant to grow, watering as needed.

❸ Observe the plant for several weeks and note how it is growing. Is it growing new leaves and getting taller, or is it unable to thrive in the soil?

❹ Record your observations in the Laboratory Notebook.

Results and Conclusions

Soils vary in their ability to support plant growth. Some soils, like clay, do not allow the water to drain, and they become hard-packed, making it difficult for plant roots to grow. Other soils, like sand, allow the water to flow through too quickly, making it difficult for roots to get enough water. Also, many soils do not have adequate nutrients or have the wrong pH to support plant growth.

13. Testing Soil

Objective

To investigate the ratio of clay, sand, silt, and organic matter in a soil sample.

Materials

pencil
ruler
jar with lid
120 ml (1/2 cup) soil sample
15 ml (1 tbsp.) water softener (e.g., Calgon liquid)
.5 liter (2 cups) of water
Super Simple Science Experiments Laboratory Notebook

Experiment

❶ Put the soil sample, water softener, and .5 liter (2 cups) of water in the jar. Secure the lid and shake vigorously to mix.

❷ Allow the contents to settle for 24 hours.

❸ With the ruler, measure the thickness of each layer.

❹ Determine the percentage of each layer by dividing the thickness of each layer by the total depth of all layers and multiplying by 100.

Results and Conclusions

Good garden soil contains 30-50% sand, 30-50% silt, 20-30% clay, and 5-10% organic matter. In your soil sample the organic matter will flow to the top and make up the top layer. The second layer from the top will be the fine grains found in clay. The third layer will contain the small grains found in silt. The sand will flow to the bottom, creating the bottom layer.

14. Making Garden Soil

simple tools

Objective

To investigate ways to improve your soil.

Materials

pencil
soil container as in Experiment 11
soil from yard
clay, silt, sand, or organic matter such as compost
small plant of the same type as in Experiment 12
Super Simple Science Experiments Laboratory Notebook

Experiment

❶ Using the information you discovered in Experiment 13, modify the ratio of a sample of your soil by adding sand, silt, clay, and/or organic matter.

❷ Take a milk carton and create a plant holder as you did in Experiment 11.

❸ Plant the same type of vegetable or herb plant as in Experiment 12 and observe how it grows.

❹ Compare your results to Experiment 12 and note if your plant grew better, the same, or worse than the plant in Experiment 12. Record you observations in your Laboratory Notebook.

Results and Conclusions

The best way to test whether your soil has improved is to grow something in it. By adjusting the ratio of the sand, clay, silt, and organic matter, you can improve the potential of your soil to sustain plant growth. However, other factors such as the pH of the soil can also affect plant growth.

15. Landforms

Objective

To investigate landforms and how they are created.

Materials

pencil
Super Simple Science Experiments Laboratory Notebook

Experiment

❶ Hike or take a field trip to a wilderness area of your choice.

❷ In your Laboratory Notebook, create a table with 5 columns and several rows. Label the top row of each column as follows: Landform, Structure, Process, Slope, and Drainage.

❸ Refer to the chart below when recording your observations about the landforms you are investigating and their structure, process, slope, and drainage.

Landform Characteristics

Structure	Process	Slope	Drainage
List the type of rock and mineral the landform is made of, such as sand, clay, granite, limestone, etc. Note if the landform has vertical, diagonal, or horizontal layers.	List all the geological activities that combined to form the landform, such as volcanic activity, earthquakes, rain, snow, wind, moving ice sheets, etc.	List the slope of the landform; for example, gently sloping, flat, steep, varied slopes.	Evaluate the drainage of the landform. For example, is there a river, creek, or seasonal arroyo nearby? Do flash floods occur, or does the land absorb the water?

Results and Conclusions

A landform is any geological structure, such as a mountain, mound, hill, cliff, river, valley, dune, lagoon, butte, ridge, etc. Landforms are created by the type of material they are made of, erosion due to weathering, and other geological activities such as volcanos or earthquakes.

16. Mechanical Weathering

simple tools

Objective

To explore how mechanical weathering contributes to landform formation.

Materials

pencil
plastic freezer container
balloon to fill with water
plaster of Paris
Super Simple Science Experiments
    Laboratory Notebook

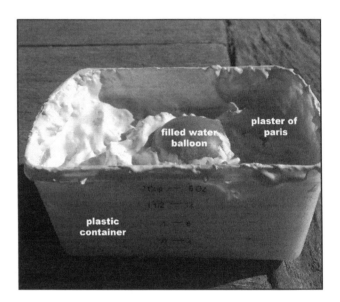

Experiment

❶ Fill the balloon with water.

❷ Following the instructions on the box, mix the plaster of Paris until you have a thick paste.

❸ Partially fill the plastic freezer container with plaster of Paris.

❹ Gently push the water balloon inside the plaster of Paris. Add plaster of Paris, if needed, until the balloon is completely covered and you have a solid block.

❺ Allow the plaster of Paris to dry. Once it is dry, place the container in the freezer and allow to freeze for 24 hours.

❻ Record your observations in your Laboratory Notebook.

Results and Conclusions

In this experiment you observed how the water balloon expands as it freezes, creating enough physical force to break the plaster of Paris. This is an illustration of mechanical weathering. Mechanical weathering occurs when rocks are broken by physical forces such as the heating and cooling of rocks and the expansion and contraction of water as it freezes and thaws.

17. Chemical Weathering

Objective

To explore how chemical weathering contributes to shaping and creating landforms.

Materials

pencil
2 pieces of chalk
2 jars
60 ml (1/4 cup) water
60 ml (1/4 cup) apple cider
   vinegar
Super Simple Science
   Experiments Laboratory
   Notebook

Experiment

❶ Place one piece of chalk in each jar.

❷ Add 60 ml (1/4 cup) of water to one jar and add 60 ml (1/4 cup) of vinegar to the other jar.

❸ Wait 30 minutes.

❹ Pour the contents of each jar out and record your observations in your Laboratory Notebook.

Results and Conclusions

Chemical weathering occurs as a result of chemical reactions. In this experiment you observed how chalk reacts chemically with vinegar. Chalk is a type of limestone made primarily of crushed shells and marine organisms. Chalk contains calcium carbonate which reacts chemically with acetic acid (vinegar) and releases carbon dioxide gas visible as bubbles. Chemical weathering occurs with many different types of rocks and is more common in areas with abundant water and warmer temperatures.

18. Landslides, Flows, and Creeps

Objective

To explore how landslides, flows, and creeps contribute to landform formation.

Materials

pencil

ruler

an area in your yard or at a park where you can make a dirt city, or go to the beach and build a sand city

garden hose with spray nozzle or a bucket of water

Super Simple Science Experiments Laboratory Notebook

Experiment

❶ Create a dirt or sand city with a mountain area on one side and a river.

❷ Using a garden hose or a bucket of water, pour water down the river. Begin with a low flow and then slowly increase the amount of water you pour through the river.

❸ Observe what happens as you increase the flow of water. If you have a garden hose with a spray nozzle, spray your city to give it some heavy "rain."

❹ Write your observations in your Laboratory Notebook.

Results and Conclusions

Building a dirt or sand city is a good way to model what happens during a landslide, flow, or creep. As you increased the amount of water running through your river and interacting with your dirt city, you likely observed sections of your city collapse into a landslide. Landslides occur when large sections of earth slide down the slope together. If your river spilled over and did not create a landslide, it may have created a flow. Flows occur more slowly than landslides and require large amounts of water. Finally, if you leave your dirt city for a few days, when you return you may observe a creep—a slow movement of material sinking or sliding downward.

19. Making a Contour Map

Objective

To map a model mountain to investigate how a contour map works.

Materials

pencil
ruler
stiff dough or modeling clay
knife
Super Simple Science Experiments Laboratory
    Notebook

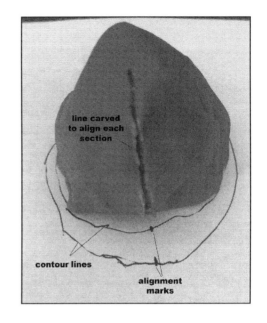

line carved to align each section

contour lines

alignment marks

Experiment

❶ Make a small mountain out of your stiff dough or clay. It can be any shape.

❷ Using the knife, carve a thin line from the top to the bottom of your small mountain.

❸ Put the bottom of the mountain on a page in your Laboratory Notebook and trace around it. Mark the place where the line you carved into the mountain intersects with your traced drawing.

❹ Turn the mountain on its side. Carefully slice a 1.25 cm (1/2 in.) section off the bottom.

❺ Place the bottom of the shortened mountain inside your previous drawing and align the carved line with the mark on your drawing. Retrace around the mountain.

❻ Repeat steps ❹-❺ until you have sliced through and traced the entire mountain.

Results and Conclusions

A contour map uses contour lines to illustrate the height and steepness of mountains and other geological features. As you traced around your model mountain, you created contour lines. Each time you sliced through the model mountain and traced around it, you created a new contour line. You can see that if you keep the depth of each of the sections equal, the contour map will represent the height of the model mountain.

20. Using a Compass

Objective

To explore how to use a compass for navigating.

Materials

pencil
compass
Super Simple Science Experiments Laboratory
    Notebook

Experiment

❶ Place the compass in your hand and observe the needle. Does it move freely as you turn the compass? Which direction is the red part of the needle pointing?

❷ With the compass in your hand rotate your body until the red part of the needle points to "N."

❸ Look up and observe your surroundings. Note where the sun is in the sky and which geological and/or man-made features are nearby. Record your observations in your Laboratory Notebook and mark this as "North."

❹ Keeping the compass in your hand, rotate your body clockwise 90 degrees. Observe what happens to the compass. Record the direction you are facing and notice where the sun is and which geological and/or man-made features are nearby. Record your observations in your Laboratory Notebook and mark this as "East."

❺ Continue to rotate your body clockwise another 90 degrees to find "South" and another 90 degrees to find "West." Repeat until you are comfortable that you can use the compass to orient yourself.

Results and Conclusions

The needle on a compass always points towards north. Many compass needles are red and black with the red part pointing north and the black part pointing south. By learning to use a compass you can tell which direction you are going in and whether you need to change directions.

21. Putting It All Together: A Day Hike

Objective

To put all your geology knowhow to the test.

Materials

pencil
backpack
hand lens
copper penny, nail, and streak plate
compass
small plastic container and spoon or garden trowel
water bottle and snack food
Super Simple Science Experiments Laboratory
    Notebook

Experiment

❶ Take a friend, parent, or teacher on a day hike. Pick a safe area where you can walk for a few hours, such as a public or national park or a local hiking trail.

❷ Using your compass, record the direction you are facing as you begin your hike. Frequently check the direction you are traveling and record it.

❸ If possible, pick up rocks and test them using the copper penny, nail, and streak plate. Using the hand lens, guess the types of rocks you observe. Record your observations. If possible, collect a soil sample, place it in the plastic container, and repeat Experiment 13 when you get home.

❹ Record any geological features you observe. Notice if there are mountains, buttes, mesas, rivers, lakes, ponds, or if there is any evidence of landslides, flows, volcanoes, or earthquakes.

Results and Conclusions

Geology can be fascinating if you know what to look for. Having some understanding of rocks, minerals, geological features, and how to navigate using a compass opens up a new way of exploring Earth!

More REAL SCIENCE-4-KIDS Books
by Rebecca W. Keller, PhD

Focus Series unit study program — each title has a Student Textbook with accompanying Laboratory Workbook, Teacher's Manual, Study Folder, Quizzes, and Recorded Lectures

Focus On Elementary Chemistry
Focus On Elementary Biology
Focus On Elementary Physics
Focus On Elementary Geology
Focus On Elementary Astronomy

Focus On Middle School Chemistry
Focus On Middle School Biology
Focus On Middle School Physics
Focus On Middle School Geology
Focus On Middle School Astronomy

Focus On High School Chemistry

Building Blocks Series yearlong study program — each Student Textbook has accompanying Laboratory Notebook, Teacher's Manual, Lesson Plan, and Quizzes

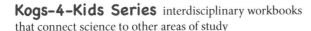

Exploring the Building Blocks of Science Book K (Activity Book)
Exploring the Building Blocks of Science Book 1
Exploring the Building Blocks of Science Book 2
Exploring the Building Blocks of Science Book 3
Exploring the Building Blocks of Science Book 4
Exploring the Building Blocks of Science Book 5
Exploring the Building Blocks of Science Book 6
Exploring the Building Blocks of Science Book 7
Exploring the Building Blocks of Science Book 8

Super Simple Science Experiments Series

21 Super Simple Chemistry Experiments
21 Super Simple Biology Experiments
21 Super Simple Physics Experiments
21 Super Simple Geology Experiments
21 Super Simple Astronomy Experiments
101 Super Simple Science Experiments

Kogs-4-Kids Series interdisciplinary workbooks that connect science to other areas of study

Physics Connects to Language
Biology Connects to Language
Chemistry Connects to Language
Geology Connects to Language
Astronomy Connects to Language

Note: A few titles may still be in production.

Gravitas Publications Inc.
www.realscience4kids.com

Made in the USA
Charleston, SC
16 May 2015